Y

IF YOU LIVE OR DIE

ALIEN INVASION

SIMON CHAPMAN

First published in 2013
by Franklin Watts

Text © Simon Chapman 2013
Illustrations by David Cousens © Franklin Watts 2013

Franklin Watts
338 Euston Road
London NW1 3BH

Franklin Watts Australia
Level 17/207 Kent Street
Sydney, NSW 2000

A CIP catalogue record for this book
is available from the British Library.

(pb) ISBN: 978 1 4451 1364 7
(Library ebook) ISBN: 978 1 4451 2565 7
(ebook) ISBN: 978 1 4451 1368 5

1 3 5 7 9 10 8 6 4 2

Printed in Great Britain

Franklin Watts is a division of Hachette Children's Books,
an Hachette UK company.
www.hachette.co.uk

This book is not like others you may have read. YOU will decide if you live or die by making choices that affect how the adventure unfolds.

Each section of this book is numbered. At the end of most sections, you will have to make a choice. The choice you make will take you to a different section of the book.

Some of your choices will help you to survive the adventure. But choose carefully! The wrong decisions could cost you your life...

If you die, then go back to the chapter number you are given and learn from your mistake.

If you choose correctly, you will survive.

CHAPTER ONE

You cannot move. Your arms are pinned to your sides by an invisible force. Your eyes are fixed wide open, dazzled by a light so bright you feel it could shine right through you. There is an alien noise, too: a static hiss from no particular place, but it is everywhere. It worms its way through your brain, your chest and every part of your body. You know that even if you could cover your ears, it wouldn't help. It's as though you are locked inside a lightning bolt, and you are terrified.

Now something is changing. Through the fizz in your head you can hear a clicking sound. There's a tingling sensation moving upwards from your feet, like a slice of electricity scanning steadily past your ankles, over your knees and into your thighs. Soon it will be going up your body. What will happen when it gets to your head?

What were you doing before this happened? Even though your brain hurts, you can remember walking home from school, through the waste ground and by some new industrial units. You were on your own, not in any particular hurry, and absorbed in a magazine as usual. That's when you saw the ball of light in the sky. Not that you took any notice at first. You only looked up when it flew past, stopped dead, and then abruptly changed course a full ninety degrees and stopped directly above your head.

It was a shining disc.

You could have run away, or hidden behind a wall, but in one moment of indecision you were frozen in the alien's beam. Face looking up to the sky, arms by your sides, you could feel your brain yelling at your legs to run.

Now you are being lifted off the ground. The beam is changing in pitch as the light scans the cavities of your lungs, then moves up your neck, tracing the curve of your jaw, your lips, your nostrils ... and moving into your brain. Memories start flashing through the TV screen of your mind, as if some viral download is extracting every file. You see school today, swimming in the sea, your mother's expression at a funeral, a car crash. Then your senses are probed. The aliens are activating tastes in your mind! Chocolate — you actually taste chocolate in your mouth — and other tastes

as well: apple juice, sour milk, chicken curry, steak pie, vomit, chips. The snippets of every flavour you have ever tasted pass by at machine-gun speed. Your mind and your mouth are awash with sensation.

Then you realise the clicking noise behind the static has stopped, like a conversation broken in mid-sentence.

You are no longer rising.

The thought "<Question>" forms in your mind.

"<What are these things?>" the static hissing seems to say.

A series of shapes and lines flash through your thoughts. Now, instead of an alien hissing noise, you can hear an alien language. Somehow you understand what is being said, as though you've downloaded the code to it.

"<Channels are open. You may reply>," it tells you. You know that what you mind-message back now could give you the chance to escape.

Survival Challenge: Escape from the Aliens

You need to control your thoughts to communicate and get free of the alien's beam — and quickly!

The decisions you make now will decide whether you live or die.

➔   To think of a visual image of you being let down to the ground, go to 47.

➔   To think of a taste again, go to 69.

➔   To think the words, "Put me down, now!", go to 26.

1.

The air judders as another jet passes overhead and then releases its missiles. The noise of them impacting on the dome is much louder now, and you risk glancing over your shoulder. The dome is completely undamaged — the force field is protecting it. The stalk raises the eye into the sky.

➔   To continue running down the street, go to 87.

➔   To head to the side of the street and into an alley for cover, go to 10.

2.

You decide that even if you could get to Ryan, there's little chance he'd listen to you. You clamber over a man, but you're still being pushed fowards. Then you spot a tree over to the left.

➜ If you want to crowd surf towards the tree, go to 64.

➜ To keep on clambering over people, away from the 'shroom, go to 52.

➜ If you decide to move with the crowd towards the 'shroom, go to 89.

3.

The alien detects you, and not even your force field can protect you from what happens next. One of the alien's legs comes down on your head, crushing you.

➜ You're dead! Get back to Chapter 6 to try again.

4.

You head back out into your street. Almost every house is on fire — even the road surface is on fire. The alien eye appears through the flames. It's still alive! The eye locks onto you. Alien words creep through your brain.

"<It is you!>" you hear it say. But your thoughts are suddenly cut off as more bombs falls from the sky and detonate around you.

➜ You have died. Get back to Chapter 3 to start again.

5.

The glass shatters but the wires hold it in place. You will not get inside this way, and now spores are floating down the alley!

➜ To use the crowbar to lever open the door before spores land on you. You'll need some luck. Choose either 46 or 68.

➜ To leave Dennis and try to escape from the alley, go to 73.

6.

On the ground, you try to push your way through people's legs. But someone steps on your hand, and then a kick knocks the breath from your lungs. You stumble, and you are quickly trampled to death by the happy crowd.

➜ Get back to Chapter 2 to try again.

7.

You bring up your shield and begin to repel the alien's force field. There is a crackle of energy as you push forward. But the shields are reacting against each other, and not in a good way! There is a flash of light and your body is engulfed in a searing heat as your shield explodes.

➜ You have failed the challenge! Get back on your feet and start again at Chapter 6.

8.

You think of apple juice, but it is hard to

remember the flavour clearly. You have risen another two metres by the time you focus on the sweet juicy taste. Then the alien's beam flickers and you stop rising. Go to 80.

9.

You turn and run down the tunnel you entered through. However, instead of opening up, the tunnel begins to close. Soon it will be too narrow to squeeze along.

→   To try to wriggle through before the tunnel closes, go to 35.

→   To go back and grab a maggot alien baby, go to 42.

10.

A blast of hot air scorches your back as a missile explodes behind you. The house you were alongside just seconds ago took the blast, not you. It collapses and you carry on down an alley, towards the backs of the houses on the next street. Several larger explosions shake the ground and you crash against the alley wall. You glance back, just as the stalk enters the alley and a larger shadow falls over you. It's the alien 'shroom! It's now above you, and so close you can feel the static tingling in your mind. You know that you might have only seconds before the alien senses you.

➜   To run back towards your house, where the alien eye is, go to 36.

➜   To carry on down the alley, towards

the houses in the next street, go to 24.

11.

You wrench your hands free, pull the grenade's pin and throw the metal ball between the slicing mouthparts. Go to 58.

12.

You push towards Ryan, passing a tree on the way. When you reach him, you pull his arm but he carries on forward without registering that you are even there. He is bigger than you and you can't stop him.

➜   To follow him into the pool of light that is flooding out beneath the stretched up dome, go to 89.

➜   To clamber over people away from the 'shroom, go to 52.

13.

You leap away from what is now clearly a UFO — an alien ship — and run between the industrial units. You hide behind some bushes, watching as the beam of light searches the ground before abruptly shutting off. Without a sound, the shining disc shoots away, up into the sky.

As you race home, you notice there is something different in your head. The static hiss in your brain is still there. You can lower its volume, but it doesn't go away. The communication with the alien flicked a switch in your mind. "<Channels are open>", the alien thoughts said, and you know that its brain link was never closed. Then — later on when you're lying on your bed playing events over in your head — you remember something else. In the last moment of contact with the alien before it dropped you, you sensed something. The alien's fear.

CHAPTER TWO

Just over a year has passed since the aliens attempted to take you. You haven't told anyone about what happened — not your parents, and certainly not your two brothers. Better to keep quiet about these things, especially when the mushrooms started to appear shortly afterwards.

Technically they aren't really mushrooms — they're silver-coloured domes or caps, about fifty metres wide. They were world news when they arrived. Seven million super-slippery mushrooms appeared, one near each centre of human population. The headlines "Alien Invasion" and "War of the Worlds" appeared in just about every news article. Panic broke out as people tried to get away from the mushrooms.

The military blasted some of the mushrooms with explosives, but nothing happened. They tried to move them with gigantic cranes, but the mushrooms couldn't be shifted; something to do with "inter-molecular forces" and "infinite mass".

Then they tried to run scientific tests, but no one could open the 'shrooms because of their protective force field. So, people were told to keep away. The authorities cordoned off the mushrooms with barriers and official notices saying not to approach or touch.

Of course, people did exactly the opposite. They reported feeling happy and

content after touching the mushrooms. And the weirdest thing of all? Pretty soon no one was bothered by them.

You said to your mum and dad that they were the ships of alien invaders. You told them that making people feel good was like some drug to calm us all down. They said you were being irrational. Your brothers were less polite.

It was pointless to argue. But you did make one decision: to be prepared. You got together a pack of food and spare clothes. When the alien mushrooms woke up, you would be ready.

Your attempted abduction and the arrival of the mushrooms happened so long ago, that it almost feels as if you imagined it. Only the tingling you get when you're near the mushrooms reminds you that you are different.

The sensation triggers unpleasant memories of the full body scan that the disc gave you. Memories of the slice of electricity passing over you, and entering your brain...

You wake up with a start after another nightmare. Something is different.

The static hiss in your head has changed slightly.

You get dressed quickly and head downstairs. Gradually, the hissing noise is "filling out" like a symphony starting with one violin, and building up as the whole orchestra joins in. The front door is wide open. Outside, people are coming out of their houses — some dressed only in their pyjamas. They are all heading for the mushroom. No one is talking, everyone is united in their silence.

"What's going on?" you ask your neighbour's daughter. But she just wanders past — it's as though you don't exist.

By the time you reach the town centre, thousands of people are there. From the looks of it, the whole town has turned out. Everyone looks happy and expectant, like the faces before a big football match. Still the only thing you can hear is the hiss in your head. Without warning, the mushroom begins to change shape. It stretches itself high off the ground, pushing out a fine stalk from its dome. The stalk has a glassy red disc on top. It sways high over the crowd and reminds you of a giant bug's eye.

Survival Challenge: In the Crowd

As the stalk rises, the crowd begins to move. Everyone shuffles forward, like the crowd at a concert. They all want to be at the front.

The decisions you make now will decide whether you live or die.

➜   If you want to move forward with everyone else, go to 30.

➜   To move backwards, go to 45.

14.

You decide that you want to get away while you still can, so you grab a branch and swing down onto the shoulders of a tall policeman. There is no reaction on his face; only the joy promised by the 'shroom.

You quickly leap onto more shoulders. You almost fall several times as people buckle beneath you. You get near to the edge of the crowd, where you can see clear ground, as you sense the static field around you changing.

→   To keep clambering over the crowd, go to 67.

→   To turn to see why the static field is changing, go to 19.

15.

You envisage the alien maggots exploding in flames, but vision is one of the senses the alien has. Your thoughts have no effect. The jelly tendrils reach out and latch onto your head, flooding your brain with thoughts, until finally the grey matter in your head explodes.

→   You have died. Pull yourself together and head back to Chapter 5.

16.

You can see two fire engines in the unlit fire station; their doors are open. In the time you have taken to look through the window, a spore has brushed against the door. It instantly spreads flat, sending out tendrils that branch out again and again. A lump at the centre of the roots starts to swell as they take in nutrients.

➜ To see what happens to the spore, go to 32.

➜ To head to the rear of the fire station to look for another way in, go to 56.

17.

You race through the house to the front door, but before you get there, the entire house collapses on top of you.

➜ You have been crushed to death. Get back to Chapter 3 to start again.

18.

Before you can move, you sense the alien's static field changing. Has it detected you?

➜ Only luck will decide, go to either 63 or 71.

19.

You turn to look at the 'shroom as the static field changes. A static voices hisses as it reaches into your brain. "<Wait. Your mind is different. Do I know you?>" Suddenly the 'shroom's stalk stretches over as the crimson "eye" hunts for you.

➜ To turn away and keep clambering over people's shoulders, go to 81.

➜ To grab hold of a lamp post and confront the eye, go to 57.

20.

As soon as you touch one tendril, more sucker onto you. Each one adds more noise into your mind. Soon this will be so loud that you won't be able to think clearly.

→ To try to break free, go to 54.

→ If you want to turn to face the crimson eye, test your luck. Go to 49 or 76.

21.

A new beam of blinding white light stabs down from the shining disc-shaped object in the sky. The beam sweeps around until it stops on one of your feet.

→ To throw yourself out of the way and run for it, go to 13.

→ To confront the shining disc with a blast of food memories, go to 85.

→ If you would rather stay still and hope the beam hasn't detected you, go to 37.

22.

You stay in the alleyway hoping the alien doesn't detect you, but when she pauses

in the street you know she's spotted you.
As you go to raise your shield you are stuck
by an enormous blast of energy fired by the
alien mother. You body turns to ash where
you stand.

➜   You've been killed! Get back to
Chapter 6. Don't let the alien mother win!

23.

You decide to wait to see what the 'shroom
does. People continue to push past, until
you think there must be a massive crush
at the front. Then there is a loud crack,
and the branch under your feet snaps. You
tumble down. Fortunately the crowd breaks
your fall, and you land on your hands and
knees on the ground. Go to 6.

24.

You run as fast as you can down the alley
and away from the eye. You pass between

23

24

two undamaged houses, before reaching the next street. A flicker of movement at the back door of the nearest one catches your attention. There's a short man waving at you. Then suddenly there is movement

ahead of you. You stop dead in your tracks. It's an alien warrior — the one you saw when you linked with the crimson eye in the town centre. It has evil-looking angled arms and legs, an armoured body and a head with a razor-cutter mouth. You can sense the malice in its mind. It wants to kill you. It wants to kill everyone. It starts to point its weapon towards you.

➜ To jump over the fence to where the man is waving, go to 60.

➜ To run up the alley towards the alien warrior with the gun, go to 65.

➜ To go back, towards the alien eye stalk in your street, go to 36.

25.

Pushing Dennis in his wheelchair, you go down a side alley to a back door, reinforced with a metal panel and a small wire-mesh-toughened glass window.

➜   To use the crowbar to try to lever the door open, go to 46.

➜   Try to smash the window, go to 5.

26.

The mind-chatter stops and you suddenly feel an electric shock pass through your brain. You are unconscious as the light beam lifts you up into the shining object.

➜   You do not survive. Go back to Chapter 1 and try again.

27.

You think of a noisy police siren. Nothing seems to happen — try something else.

➜   To think of an image of alien maggots exploding in flames, go to 15.

➜   To think about when you broke your arm falling off your bike, go to 61.

➜   To think of the smell in your nostrils, go to 78.

28.

You duck down behind a car just as a missile explodes at the end of your street. You lean up against the car door as debris rains down on you. The roar of a plane above you fills your ears.

➜ To run and hide in the alley, go to 72.

➜ If you want to head back out into your street, where you came from, go to 4.

➜ To run through the alley to the next street, go to 24.

29.

You send out a mind blast: a scramble of random throughts to confuse the alien mother. But she was prepared for this and pulls you closer with her grabber arms. You are still mind-blasting when her knife-sharp mouthparts start slicing through your head.

➜ You've been minced up! Go back to Chapter 6 and try again.

30.

An alien mind message is filling your head. "<Come, join us. Live in endless happiness>," it says. Ahead of you, the sides of the 'shroom are shrinking back into a field of light, and you feel happy. But, unlike all the others who are being taken in, you know this is false.

➜ To continue forward with the crowd and enter into the 'shroom, go to 89.

➜ If you want to try to move backwards, away from the 'shroom, go to 45.

31.

Your memory download continues. This is just like what happened a year ago when the UFO tried to abduct you. There was a human sense that the alien in control could not understand. You have another four senses. You know what you have to do: find the right sense to crash the alien's programming!

→ If you think of the sound of a really loud siren, go to 27.

→ If you think of a visual image of alien maggots exploding in flames, go to 15.

→ To think about when you broke your arm, go to 61.

→ To think of the smell in your nostrils, go to 78.

32.

What happens next is too quick for you to react to. Perhaps triggered by your body heat, a nearby floating spore explodes, shooting out a mass of tendrils that instantly seek out your flesh, burrowing in straight for your heart and vital organs.

→ You have become alien plant food! Get back to Chapter 4 — don't let the aliens take over Earth!

33.

While the alien is occupied with the soldiers, you move out from behind the car until you are close enough to touch the alien's shield.

➜   To use your shield to repel the alien's force field, go to 7.

➜   To merge your shield with its force field, go to 75.

34.

You race along, zigzagging between confused people. You spot a narrow alleyway and race towards it. You glance back and see the eye stalk retracting and the inward movement of the crowd restarting. From the safety of the alleyway you watch as everyone slowly disappears into the light. Your family has gone, but you got away.

CHAPTER THREE

Your lungs feel as though they are on fire by the time you reach your house. From under your bed you snatch up the small pack of provisions that you prepared. You knew this day would come. Why did no one listen? Your parents, your brothers, your friends: everyone has gone. You know you have to put any thoughts about their loss aside if you are to survive.

There is something about you that the aliens don't know how to deal with; you are convinced of that. First there was the attempted abduction, and the way the beam could not hold you. Then there's what happened in the town centre. When the red eye sensor on the stalk had you fixed in its glare, the 'shroom could not maintain its mind control over the hundreds of people. Something about you frightens whatever is controlling the 'shroom and that makes you special. Your mind is still free! You can fight back! Of course, there's a major downside to whatever power you may have. If you truly are dangerous to it, then the alien intelligence controlling the 'shroom will want you dead.

You decide you are going to have to keep out of sight, just as there is a massive explosion. The house rocks, windows implode and you dive to the floor. As you get to your feet there is a roar from outside. You grab your rucksack and head out into the street.

Overhead, you see the angluar shapes of three airforce fighter jets. Further down the street, towards the direction of the alien 'shroom, the street is ablaze. Smoke and dust fills the air. A plane has obviously dropped a massive bomb on the 'shroom. The military must be trying to fight back! You're not the only person left! More explosions rock the ground, and looking up again you see missiles streaking across the sky towards the 'shroom. You can only see its silvery stem stretching up as the crimson eye searches for targets. The air vibrates with each missile impact. The fighter jets circle around for another strike and you jump up, punching the air. "Go get it!" But something is bothering you. What about the force field? Would that stop any sort of damage, just like it stopped the military when they tried to destroy the 'shrooms when they first arrived?

You decide it's not safe here. Your street is turning into a war zone. But just as you go to head off away from the fire, something happens to the fighter jets. The lead plane suddenly spins out of control, and the jets of the two wingmen spiral up into the sky and loop over. You watch in horror as the lead jet disappears into the fire, and the two remaining planes bank round. The crimson eye tracks one, then it flashes bright red. A stream of energy shoots from the eye and the jet disappears in a ball of flame. The last jet turns steeply, clearly not under the control of the pilot, and roars towards the ground. Only slowly do you realise it's heading straight for you! Instinctively you duck. The jet plunges into a house across the street and explodes. The noise is almost deafening, and the blast throws you to the

ground. You strike your head and pass out.

Survival Challenge: On the Run

You wake to the smell of burning fuel, and remember the jet crashing. Quickly, you grab your rucksack and stagger to your feet. You freeze. The alien eye from the 'shroom is snaking down the street, and not much further behind it is the dome of the 'shroom. It's moving up from the town centre! It can fly! The stalk is panning back and forth now, looking for something. And then you realise what it's scanning for — you! You decide to do the only thing you can — run!

The decisions you make now will decide whether you live or die.

➜ If you decide to run down the middle of the street, go to 1.

➜ If you decide to stay closer to the buildings, go to 43.

35.

In a desperate attempt to get away from the aliens you push further down the tunnel. But eventually you become trapped. The tunnel walls close in around you quickly crushing you to death.

➜   You have been killed by the mothership. Get back to Chapter 5.

36.

You move slowly back down the alley, towards the eye, hoping that it won't detect you. But as soon as you get close to it, the alien's thoughts fill your mind.

"<I know you>," the voice says as the eye cranes up and over you. "<And you will die>." The last thing you see before you are incinerated by the plasma beam is a flash of red light.

➜   The aliens have won! Get back to Chapter 3 to put a stop to their plans.

37.

You stay still in the hope the beam can't detect you. But it locks onto you, dragging you up into the ship.

➜   You don't survive the alien experiments. Get back to Chapter 1.

38.

Attracted by your warmth, a floating spore is closing in on you. You push with all your strength at the end of the crowbar, and the door shifts. The spore is so close you can see the pink skin beneath the outer fuzz rippling as the rootlets inside ready themselves to burst out. Dennis throws his jacket to knock the floating ball off course. Go to 62.

39.

You try to push through the crowd, but

37

38

39

there are simply too many people. Shoving against them is like pushing against a brick wall. You are swept forward towards the 'shroom dome. Go to 89.

40.

Sensing the warmth of your hand, three rootlets latch onto it. Within seconds it is a writhing mass of tendrils, burrowing in for nutrients to renew their lifecycle. The pain is excruciating as they track up your veins and penetrate your heart, killing you.

➜ You have become plant food! Pull yourself together and get back to Chapter 4.

41.

Mmmmm... You think about the taste of chocolate melting in your mouth. The memory is good enough to make your mouth water. Taste is a sense the alien intelligence behind the scan does not understand. Its thoughts swirl into a message. "<I cannot taste>," the alien thoughts say. "<Therefore taste does not exist. Therefore you do not exist>."

The beam is broken and you drop to the ground, landing easily.

➜   If you want to run, go to 13.

➜   If you decide to stay where you are, go to 21.

42.

You reach out and sink your fingers into the jelly-like matter. With a slurping sound you tear the alien maggot from the wall. It wiggles feebly. You feel it probing your thoughts, but you also feel its thoughts. It hates you. It fears you too. It can sense light, thoughts and touch, but not any other senses. These extra inputs could overload its thoughts. The crimson eye is still turning to face you. The jelly sacks of

the other alien maggots are now extruding
long tendrils which are trying to sucker
onto your head.

➜ To touch the tendrils, go to 20.

➜ If you want to turn to face the
crimson eye, go to 49.

➜ To grab the eye, go to 76.

43.

You decide that running along closer to the buildings will be safer. Another jet crashes into the ground further up the street. The alien crimson eye fires a blast towards you and the house next to you bursts into flame. Tiles, broken bricks and glass shards rain down on you.

➡   Go to 51.

44.

The grenade hits the alien's force field, falls to the ground and then explodes. The alien is unharmed. It turns its weapons and shoots at the ground in front of you. A massive crater opens up. You try to leap out of the way, but nothing can stop you falling down into the sewer far below.

➡   You die slowly in the stinking water underground. Clean up your act — get back to Chapter 6.

45.

You turn to move backwards. While you've been watching the stalk rise into the air, the crowd has closed in around you. You try to push your way between the people, but they are tightly packed. They smile at you, some stroke your hair and face. You try to climb up them — you've seen people crowd surf at gigs — but then you spot your older brother, Ryan. He's some way off, nearer the 'shroom. On his face is an expression of absolute contentment.

➜ If you want to try to push through the crowd to get Ryan away from the 'shroom, go to 12.

➜ If you decide to forget Ryan, and carry on trying to move away from the 'shroom, go to 2.

➜ If you'd rather join Ryan, and see if you can experience happiness, go to 89.

46.

You start to lever open the door, but it is metal — to deter people from breaking in — and the lock is very strong. A floating spore brushes against Dennis's wheelchair, sending out a mass of tiny roots that work their way into the metal framework.

➜   To brush off the tendrils, go to 40.

➜   To leave Dennis and escape out of the alley, go to 73.

➜   To pull Dennis out of his wheelchair, go to 79.

47.

There's a slight glitch in the beam, but you are still rising.

➜   If you carry on thinking of visual images, go to 55.

➜   To think of a taste, go to 69.

➜   To think the words, "put me down, now!", go to 26.

48.

As you go to move, your alien-altered senses pick up a power surge. The crimson eye crackles and begins to glow with what looks like super-hot energy. Only luck will decide whether you can survive now.

➜ Go to 70 or 86.

49.

You go to move but the alien eye swings round. It knocks you down with a crunching blow, before turning your body into alien baby food.

➜ You have been turned into liquid mush. Go to Chapter 5 to try again.

50.

You pull the man and his wheelchair down the cellar steps as the house shakes. You stumble and land heavily as dust and the noise of crashing bricks fills the air.

CHAPTER FOUR

The disabled man, in whose cellar you find yourself, is called Dennis Mackenzie. Like everyone else he heard the alien messages in his brain and, without really understanding why, he tried to get out of his house. By the time he'd got into his wheelchair, the messages stopped. You explain what happened to you, including the attempted abduction.

"Something about you is like a virus to it," he says. "I think you can upset its thought processes. I'm sure that whatever ability you have it's something important enough that the army or government, or whoever is in charge, needs to know."

"You mean there are still people out there?"

"Yes. Quite a few. I was listening to my radio before the 'shrooms started moving. The announcer said that all over the world they were opening up and calling people, but that some people weren't affected. And that's why I think you are important," he says after a short pause. "We have to contact the authorities. Telephones don't work, so we need to find a radio transmitter."

"They have radios in fire engines," you suggest. "There's a fire station near here... but, I wouldn't know how to work their radios even if I could get in there."

"No need to worry about that," Dennis assures you. "I'll make them work. You just have to get me there. I'm sure we can knock my wheelchair back into shape and, as for breaking in, I have a crowbar and a torch we can take with us."

You force open the cellar doors and the two of you set off shortly after sunset. It's oddly quiet — and dark — out in the bomb-shattered streets. Every street light is off. The whole town is empty. Even the 'shroom seems to have gone.

It's not easy pushing Dennis in the wheelchair. When you get to smooth patches of road you can whizz along quickly, but since the bombing, whole sections are covered with rubble and these are difficult to get around.

You're nearly at the fire station when the torch Dennis is holding picks out

what look like snowflakes floating in the
sky. But, these flakes are big — football-
sized — and pink and fluffy. One brushes
against a building. The instant it makes
contact, it pops open. Rootlets burst out

in all directions and the ones that hit the brickwork spread, branch out and start burrowing in. You realise what they are: seed pods or spores. You must get into the shelter of the fire station right now.

Survival Challenge: The Fire Station

At the front of the station are the large sliding doors that the fire engines exit from. These are closed and, even with your crowbar, there is no chance of you getting in — though there are windows which you can look through to see what's inside.

The decisions you make now will decide whether you live or die.

➡ To look through the windows, go to 16.
➡ To go round to the back of the fire station, go to 25.

51.

You stagger along but manage to stay on your feet as the shockwave shakes the ground. Quickly, you hold your rucksack up over your head as dust and debris fill the air. You feel bits of brick strike you, but you keep running. Another jet screams overhead, firing its missiles down towards the dome.

➜ If you want to run down an alley between the houses, go to 10.

➜ If you decide to chance it out in the open, go to 87.

52.

You climb up and clamber over people, but then you feel your foot get snagged. Someone has grabbed you! More hands grab you and pull you back down into the crowd. One woman with a daft grin, who had been pushing a shopping trolley, hugs you tightly, but you twist out of her grasp.

➡   If you want to shove the trolley towards her, go to 74.

➡   To get back over to the tree, go to 64.

➡   To try to push your way through the crowd, go to 39.

53.

The alien moves down the street until it is level with the alley where you are hiding.

➡   To throw your grenade at it, go to 44.

➡   To duck behind a car as the alien goes past, go to 18.

➡   To stay in the alleyway, go to 22.

54.

You try to break free but the tendrils fill the room. They sucker into your skin, through your eyes and into your brain.

➡   You have died. Don't be a sucker! Get back to Chapter 5 to start again.

55.

You carry on thinking of different visual images: your first swimming medal, your bike, your mum, your best friend. But the shining disc's white beam continues to pull you up until you pass between a set of doors. They close behind you, plunging you into darkness. That feeling of floating is the last feeling you ever have. You do not survive the alien experiments.

➜   Go back to Chapter 1 to try again.

56.

The air is full of spores. Have you left it too late to get to the back of the fire station?

➜   Only luck will decide if you survive. Go to 25 or 32.

57.

You steady yourself as the eye gets closer. Then you think, "YES, you do know me!" in your mind. You feel your brainwaves blast the alien voice. The red eye stops moving. Then you sense a quieter message. It's a question swirling around in the alien's thoughts. An answer comes back swiftly and clearly. It is an order. "<Kill the human!>" the voice says. Go to 48.

58.

It does not go off! It must have a time delay fuse.

➡   To fight back against the alien mother, go to 66.

➡   To risk activating your force field inside the alien's defences, go to 92.

59.

While you're trying to think of other tastes, the light beam pulls you up into the alien ship. It is the last time anyone sees you.

➡   Go back to Chapter 1.

60.

You jump over the fence as the man opens the door. "In here," he shouts. You dive through the door as a blast of plasma scorches the air above you. You plough into the man. He isn't short, he is sitting in a wheelchair. The two of you crash into the wall inside. "Quick! Into the cellar," he shouts, pointing at an open doorway as his house starts to collapse. "Help me!"

➜   To pull the man down into his cellar, go to 50.

➜   To leave him and get down into the cellar yourself, go to 83.

➜   To race through the house to the front door, go to 17.

61.

"<Pain>," the voice says. "<It is a sense and a weakness we know humans have>." The maggot tendrils are closing in...

→ To think of an image of alien maggots exploding in flames, go to 15.

→ To think of the smell in your nostrils, go to 78.

62.

Suddenly, with a crack, the door gives way and, as rootlets tear into the cloth of Dennis's coat, you drag him inside and wedge the door shut with the crowbar.

CHAPTER FIVE

You know you can't stay here for long — it isn't safe. Dennis is in the office with the two-way radio, calling for help. Calling for anyone.

"Mayday. Mayday," he repeats. "Is anyone there? Over."

So far there has been no answer.

You can't see the alien roots staying on the outside for that long. They've already covered the windows, and some have started to creep through the gaps underneath and at the sides of the fire station's doors.

"The aliens are changing the atmosphere," Dennis says. "They're making the Earth their own planet, making it habitable for them, kicking us out." You hear Dennis coughing.

For a while now, you've felt the alien presence getting stronger in your mind.

"It's searching for me," you say out loud as you walk into the office. "I can feel it in my mind and I know it's getting closer. Its thoughts are getting stronger." Dennis puts down the microphone and looks you in the eye.

"I have to get to the 'shroom," you blurt out suddenly. "There are things there that the alien is concerned about. Perhaps I can use them to defeat it."

"We can't walk, and I can't drive," Dennis says. "But I could change gear if you press the pedals and steer. But how will you find the 'shroom?"

"I can't explain, but I know where it is. Like I know whatever is in control is closing in on us. It's why we have to go."

You help Dennis up into the cab of the fire engine and, after a quick practice using the clutch and accelerator pedals, you force the vehicle out through the closed fire station door. You hurtle forward, bouncing off parked cars and bumping over roots, but you keep going. In your mind you can see the alien 'shroom in the distance. Soon the silvery dome comes into view through the pink fuzz that covers the ground and every building now that the spores have landed. You come to a stop by a round opening in the side of the 'shroom. You look back at Dennis.

"It's OK," he says. "I'll wait here. It's not like I've got to be anywhere else," he jokes. "Remember: you have some ability that these aliens fear. Go and use it."

It feels like you are entering the cone of a trumpet. The tunnel looks like it's narrowing but, as you make your way forward, it always stays large enough for you to walk through. As it flexes, the walls glow and light the way ahead. The air is becoming harder to breathe and has a strange scent of rotten meat and fruit mixed together. This must be the air that the aliens breathe.

The tunnel opens out into a chamber, though you're not sure whether you walked into it or if the walls just peeled back to form the room. It is shaped like the inside of a giant egg with tunnels joining from the sides, ceiling and floor. These tunnels close up leaving you with only one exit — the way you've just come. In the centre of the chamber is a dull crimson eye which hangs from the ceiling. Stuck around the curving walls are about twenty cushion-sized blobs of clear jelly. You take a closer look. Inside the jelly sacks are what look like baby aliens — they wriggle like maggots as you get closer. You can make out the outlines of limbs, multiple eyes and mouthparts that have not yet hardened. Slowly the static hum of their mind messages starts. They want to kill you, but you also sense confusion and fear. Wincing with disgust, you reach over and touch one of the jelly blobs. The larval alien waggles its arms, and extends one towards your hand. You slap it away and feel its pain; the static chatter cuts and you sense interest or confusion, a thought message similar to

when the disc dropped you on that first
encounter so long ago.

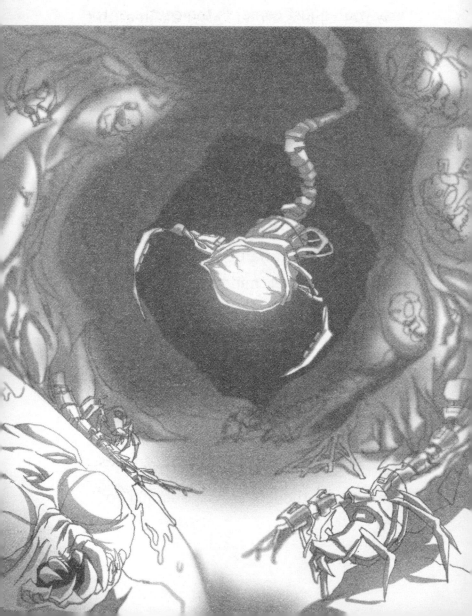

Survival Challenge: The Mothership

The static noise grows louder again as the crimson eye turns towards you.

The decisions you make now will decide whether you live or die.

➔ If you want to pull a larval alien off the wall, go to 42.

➔ If you want to run away down the tunnel you entered, go to 9.

➔ If you want to grab the crimson eye, go to 76.

63.

You've been unlucky! The alien mother detects you! Without your shield up, one blast from her plasma guns is all it takes...

➔ You're dead. Get back to Chapter 6.

64.

You leap up and manage to squirm your way across the sea of heads and shoulders to the tree. Its shelter gives you a breathing space where you can consider what to do.

➜   If you wish to climb up the tree to get a better view, go to 82.

➜   If you want to escape from the 'shroom by worming your way between people's legs, go to 6.

➜   If you want to try to push your way through the crowd, go to 39.

65.

You run towards the alien warrior, but it fires a ball of charged purple plasma at you from its weapon. You take the full impact of the blast and it punches a hole through your body. You collapse to the ground in agony as you feel the alien invade your mind. "<This planet is ours now, human

scum>," it says, just before you die.

➜ You made a brave choice, but it was the wrong one. Don't let the aliens win. Get back to Chapter 3 to start again.

66.

You claw at the alien mother with your hands, when the grenade explodes. The blast tears you and the alien to pieces.

➜ You killed the alien mother — but you're dead too! Get back to Chapter 6 to finish the job properly.

67.

The people at the outer edge of the crowd are weaker and smaller — old women who were pushed aside — and children, several of whom you recognise. You cannot crowd surf here. You jump down onto the ground and you barge your way through. Behind, you can sense the 'shroom's central stalk bending over and stretching towards you.

66

67

The alien voice fills your head again.

"<Wait! I know you>", it says. "<You are different.>" The people stop moving around you. Maybe the alien cannot concentrate on you and control them at the same time. You can almost "see" the alien behind you; ugly jointed arms, a mouth of swirling razor cutters, bulbous red eyes with a bitter hatred for the human race. Then, suddenly, the mind contact is lost.

➜   If you want to turn around to face the crimson eye, go to 48.

➜   If you would rather keep running away, go to 34.

68.
You've wasted too much time. The floating spores are all around you. Go to 32.

69.
You decide to think of another taste.

➜   To think of chocolate flavour, go to 41.

→ To think of apple flavour, go to 8.

→ To think of the taste of vomit, go to 91.

70.

The air around you sparks and a blast of fiery energy shoots out of the crimson eye. It singes your clothes and hair, but it misses! A building behind you explodes as the plasma blast strikes. Windows shatter and brick debris falls around you. You run. Go to 34.

71.

The alien doesn't see you move, and keeping your body close to the ground you make it to a car. A platoon of soldiers are engaging the alien at close range with machine guns and a flame-thrower. Their weapons have no effect; all of their fire bounces harmlessly off its force field. The alien turns its own weapons on them, and begins to incinerate them.

➜ To run away from the alien, go to 3.

➜ To get closer to the alien's force field shield, go to 33.

72.

You decide run and hide in the alley. The noise of the plane fills your ears until there is a sudden flash above you and the walls crash down around you.

➜ You have been crushed to death. Dust yourself down and get back to Chapter 3.

73.

You run up the alley, turning to see Dennis as he is engulfed by a mass of tendrils. Go to 32.

74.

You shove the trolley towards the woman but it's no use; the weight of the crowd around you pushes you, her and the trolley towards the 'shroom. Go to 89.

75.

Your force field merges with the alien's as they touch. You are now unshielded but inside the alien's force field! You are too close for her to use her plasma blasters, but she still has grabber arms and that mincer mouth. Her arms catch you and pass you up towards the spinning cutters.

"<I know you. You killed my children. Now it's your turn to die>," her voice says.

73

74

75

Her mouth blades are whirring an arm's length from your face.

→ To mind blast the alien back, go to 29.

→ To throw the grenade into her mouth, go to 11.

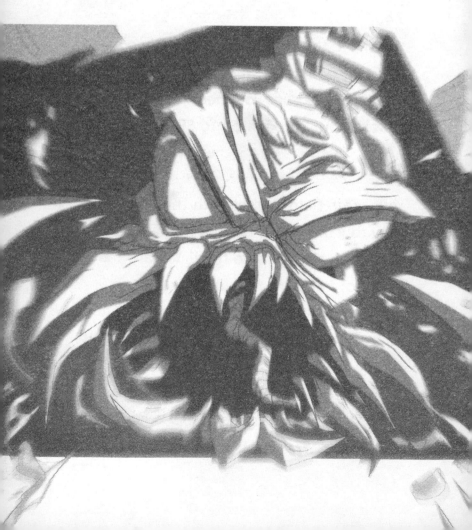

76.

As the eye turns, you grab hold of it. It doesn't just watch over the babies, it's a communication device, too. You feel your brain connect with the mother alien mind.

"<It's you>," says the alien voice. "<You cannot exist. You must die.>" Through the connection the alien begins to download your mind, slicing thoughts out of your head. All this time, the jelly sacks nearest to you are sending out tendrils.

➜ To let go of the eye and swat the tendrils away, go to 49.

➜ To stay connected with the eye, go to 31.

77.

You hold onto the eye as the crimson light fades, and continue to bombard the alien mother with memories of smells. Your brain is throbbing, but she is no match for your mental powers. The baby aliens begin to drop from the walls. The pain in your head becomes intense, until suddenly the eye fades to white and the room explodes in a shower of alien goo.

CHAPTER SIX

You wake up covered in alien larval slime. It coats your body like a second skin, even going into your mouth, nostrils and eyes; yet you can see and you can breathe. For a minute, you are gripped with pure panic.

"Get off me!" you yell through the transparent membrane, flailing your arms around, ripping at the gooey jelly. And it slides off, like it knows you wanted it to, leaving you clean and dry. You get to your feet, but you don't feel ... normal. Something has changed. You reach out with your hand and a hole opens in the wall of the chamber.

For a moment you stop and try to understand the rush of new sensations that your brain is processing. Absorbing the alien slime has given you special powers. It's as if you are part of the 'shroom now. You can control the shape and form of its surfaces and sense everything around it.

Your expanded senses are detecting life forms outside the 'shroom; human soldiers and alien warriors. You can feel the presence of the alien mother outside the 'shroom too. She is heavily shielded, but using up her energy reserves fast. She is desperate to get to you. She wants to kill you.

You step through the door, down a passage and out of the 'shroom. Outside it's a war zone. Soldiers are battling with alien warriors. The air is filled with bullets and purple plasma blasts. You spook a soldier in front of you and he turns and shoots at you without hestitating. You instinctively duck and hold up your hand, forming a shining layer around

you. You've created a force field! The bullets hit the shield and drop to the ground.

The soldier realises his mistake — you are a human — but how did you stop the bullets? The soldier looks confused.

"Where did you come from?" he asks, regaining his composure.

"I need to get to the mother alien!" you shout.

"No way! We need to get you somewhere safe." The soldier goes to grab you, but you wave your arm to enclose yourself completely in a shield. You can't let him take you. His hands bounce off and you turn towards the battle. You have to find the alien mother before it reaches the 'shroom.

Finding the alien mother is easier than you thought — you just follow the sound of people screaming. She is only a few streets away. The enormous beast strides towards the 'shroom on her strangely jointed legs. Soldiers with rocket launchers blast the alien, but her shield holds firm. She fires a series a plasma blasts from weapon pods mounted on her arms and the soldiers are easily cut down.

You crouch in an alleyway, releasing your shield as it begins to drain your energy. There is a soldier propped up against the wall. He is clearly badly injured, but he is smiling. He holds out his hand.

"It's my last one," he says slowly. "Make it count."

You nod and take the grenade.

Survival Challenge: The Final Fight

If you are going to stop the alien mother, you're going to have to get past her shield first.

The decisions you make now will decide whether you live or die.

➜   To raise your shield and run to a bomb crater in the street, go to 88.

➜   If you don't want to raise your shield, and decide to wait to see what happens next, go to 53.

78.

Panic surges out of the controlling alien's mind. It does not understand the sense of smell. Your link through the crimson eye has allowed you to put those confusing thoughts right into its brain. You feel its mind control falter. The baby alien tendrils become limp and dangle uselessly. The light in the communication eye fades.

➜   To break the connection and try to get away while the alien maggots are stunned, go to 49.

➜   To use your connection with the eye to continue your mind assault on the mother alien's mind, go to 90.

79.

You pull Dennis out of his wheelchair as it becomes covered with a mass of growing rootlets. You lower Dennis to the ground.

➜ To keep levering the door, go to 38.

➜ To give up with the door, and run up the alley to save yourself, go to 73.

80.

The beam disappears and you fall about three metres, landing heavily before rolling to one side. Go to 21.

81.

You turn away from the eye as it searches for you, and continue to crowd surf away from the 'shroom. Go to 67.

82.

As you climb into the tree's branches, you can feel them straining with your weight.

From up here, you can see it's not far to get to edge of the crowd, away from the 'shroom.

➜ To wait up here to see what the 'shroom does next, go to 23.

➜ To clamber across people's shoulders and heads to get away, go to 14.

83.

You rush over to the open cellar door. "Don't leave me here!" the man shouts at you. You turn to look at him before stepping down into the cellar. There is a smashing sound above you as the house collapses. The stairs shake and you slip on a step, tumbling to the bottom. There is a terrible crack, and you briefly feel a searing pain in your back and neck. Slowly, blackness creeps into the edges of your vision, and light fades, forever.

➜ You have died. Get back to Chapter 3 to start again.

84.

Those doubts in your mind gave the mother alien hope. A bolt of pain surges through your brain — and literally 'blows your mind'.

➜ You have been defeated by the alien mother. Get back to Chapter 5.

85.

You try to blast food memories at the disc as the light from the beam covers your body. It begins to pull you up again.

➜ This is the last time you are ever seen on Earth... Go back to Chapter 1.

86.

The air around you sparks and a blast of fiery energy shoots out of the crimson eye. The ripple of energy catches you straight in the back, and in a flash your body is reduced to a mass of superheated atoms.

➜ You were unlucky this time. Give it another shot back at Chapter 2.

84

85

86

87.

You continue running down the street. Heat scorches your face and hair as a charged-up beam of plasma flashes overhead and demolishes a house further up the street. You keep running. At the edge of your vision, you see the stalk is directing its weapon at the fighter plane.

➡   To get out of sight quickly, go to 28.

➡   To hide in an alley further along the street, go to 72.

88.

You wave your arm and the force field encircles your body. You rush out into the street, but the alien mother quickly spots you and fires off blasts of energy. The shots are absorbed by your shield and you make it to the cover of a bomb crater, just a grenade-throw-away from the monster's towering form.

→ To throw your grenade at the alien mother, go to 44.

→ To stay in the crater and repel its shots with your shield, go to 3.

→ To get out of the crater and duck behind a car, go to 71.

89.

Amongst all the humans squeezing together to get into the brightness under the 'shroom, you are the only one who realises that the thoughts in your mind are just the drugging mind control of an alien race. But you've left it too late. You are no longer in control of your body. While you scream and thrash around in the prison of your mind, your legs move you forward towards the dome. Slowly, your mind begins to relax with the thought that soon you will be dead.

→ You have died. Get back to Chapter 2 to start again.

90.

You go on the offensive and attack the mother alien's mind through the connection. You pick memories of the strongest smells: your aunt's rose-scented perfume, the stink of dog poo on your shoe, the smell of cabbage cooking, cut grass, curry, farts, cheese. The eye begins to thrash around in an attempt to break the connection. You can feel the pain of the alien controlling it.

➜ If you decide you've hurt the alien enough, go to 84.

➜ To press on with your mind assault, go to 77.

91.

You think of the last time you vomited — when you had a stomach bug. But then you try to remember the flavour. It was a complicated taste, with bad memories, and not one you can remember easily. Go to 59.

92.

You activate your force field just as the grenade explodes. The alien's innards spew out through her mouthparts, splattering your shield. You break free from the alien mother's grip as she pitches to one side. Her angular legs buckle and you jump down to the street. The destroyed alien crashes down, dead.

CHAPTER SEVEN

Shimmering in your force field, you stare at the alien you defeated. With the mother alien now dead, you assume control of her invasion fleet with your mind. You can feel your warriors, thousands and thousands of them, waiting for your command.

Some part of your enhanced senses picks up human life forms. It is Dennis and he has other people with him. Dennis is propped up between two soldiers. With them is the soldier who shot at you earlier. He looks slightly scared of you now. You don't wait for him to speak.

"Don't worry. I'm in control of the alien invasion now. Tell the soldiers to stand down. You have nothing to fear."

"So that's it then?" you hear Dennis say. "We survived?"

You smile, looking around at the devastation. "Yes, Dennis. It's over."

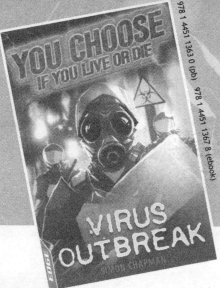